Pirate Pickle and the White Balloon

Written by Ann Burg
Illustrated by Marilyn Janovitz

Children's Press
An imprint of Scholastic Inc.
New York • Toronto • London • Auckland • Sydney
Mexico City • New Delhi • Hong Kong
Danbury, Connecticut

For Celia, who made every day an adventure.
—A. B.

Reading Consultant

Cecilia Minden-Cupp, *PhD*
Former Director of the Language and Literacy Program
Harvard Graduate School of Education
Cambridge, Massachusetts

Cover design: The Design Lab
Interior design: Herman Adler

Library of Congress Cataloging-in-Publication Data

Burg, Ann E.
Pirate Pickle and the white balloon / by Ann Burg; illustrated by Marilyn Janovitz; reading consultant, Cecilia Minden-Cupp.
p. cm. — (A rookie reader : opposites)
ISBN-13: 978-0-531-17544-6 (lib. bdg.) 978-0-531-17778-5 (pbk.)
ISBN-10: 0-531-17544-8 (lib. bdg.) 0-531-17778-5 (pbk.)
1. English language—Synonyms and antonyms—Juvenile literature.
I. Janovitz, Marilyn, ill. II. Title. III. Series.
PE1591.B78 2007
428.1—dc22 2006027033

Printed in China.

1 2 3 4 5 6 7 8 9 10 R 17 16 15 14 13 12 11 10 09 08 62

My white balloon is lost.

Wherever can it be?

I’ve searched all across the land.
Maybe it floated out to sea!

I know a certain pirate.
He wears a black patch on his eye.

Maybe he grabbed my white balloon as it floated through the sky.

Maybe my balloon is trapped, and I must set it free!

I'm not afraid no matter what.
I'm as brave as brave can be!

I will sail all day.

I will sail all night.

Then I will sail over the waves
and under the moon.

I will sail forever
to find my balloon.

When I find Pirate Pickle, I will roar,
"That balloon's mine, not yours!"

Then I will float over the waves and under the moon.

I will float back home with my balloon.

My white balloon!

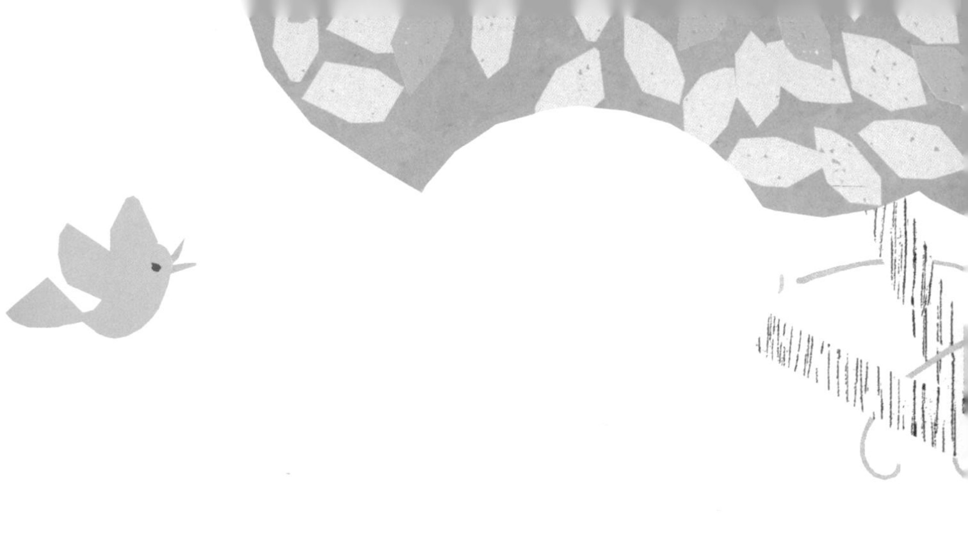

It's stuck in my neighbor's tree!

Excuse me, Mr. Pickle. . . .

Please get it down for me.

Word List (82 words)

(Words in **bold** are used as opposites.)

a	eye	it's	not	th
across	**find**	I've	on	th
afraid	float	know	**out**	thro
all	floated	**land**	**over**	t
and	for	**lost**	patch	**trap**
as	forever	matter	pickle	tr
back	**free**	maybe	pirate	**un**
balloon	get	me	please	wa
balloon's	grabbed	**mine**	roar	we
be	he	moon	sail	wh
black	his	Mr.	**sea**	wh
brave	home	must	searched	whe
can	I	my	set	**wh**
certain	I'm	neighbor's	sky	w
day	**in**	**night**	stuck	w
down	is	no	that	**yo**
excuse	it			

About the Author

Ann Burg grew up writing stories for her family and her friends. She wr
articles for newspapers and has always kept a journal. This is her seve
children's book but her drawers are stuffed with many more stories an
poems. Ann lives in upstate New York with her husband, two children,
one dog, and one very special bear.

About the Illustrator

Marilyn Janovitz's work, in a variety of styles and mediums, has been us
advertising, editorial, and textile design. She is the author-illustrator of
books for children including *Look Out Bird!*, *Is It Time?*, and *What Cou*
Keeping Santa? Marilyn works in her closet-sized studio where she can
Empire State Building twenty blocks away.